Dedicated to those who spread their love to others daily
and brighten the lives of those they touch...
who brighten the lives of those they touch....

Written by Susan Horowitz, Ph.D.

Library of Congress Cataloging-in-Publication

Helzberg, Barnett, 1933-
I am loved / written by Barnett Helzbe
illustrated by Steve Harmon p. cm.
ISBN 0-9726504-5-8 (alk. paper)
1. Love. 1. Title

BF575.L8H3795 2005
152.4'1 --dc22

2004061549

For Jennifer,

S.H.

I AM LOVED® is a registered trademark of the Shirley and Barnett Helzberg Foundation.
© 2005 TRISTAN Publishing, Inc.

TRISTAN Publishing
2300 Louisiana Ave., North
Suite B
Golden Valley, MN 55427

ISBN 0-9726504-5-8
Printed in China
First Printing

Please visit www.tristanpublishing.com

I AM LOVED®

Inspired by Shirley and Barnett Helzberg Jr.
Illustrated by Steve Harmon

TRISTAN Publishing

In the seasons of our lives,
from the start till journey ends

We are kindergarten playmates
and then old familiar friends

Whisper secrets, share a fear,
start to giggle, wipe a tear

When we're opening our hearts,
we can feel: "I am loved."

$\mathscr{D}$eep inside, we're grown-up children
clinging to a teddy bear

$\mathscr{A}$s we hug one in our arms,
we find some sweet comfort there

We are only girls and boys, older now with different toys

$\mathcal{A}$nd our hearts have just one yearning – to feel: "I am loved."

Every golden band and bracelet,
every jewel that we prize

Finds its truest worth when it
can bring a sparkle to our eyes

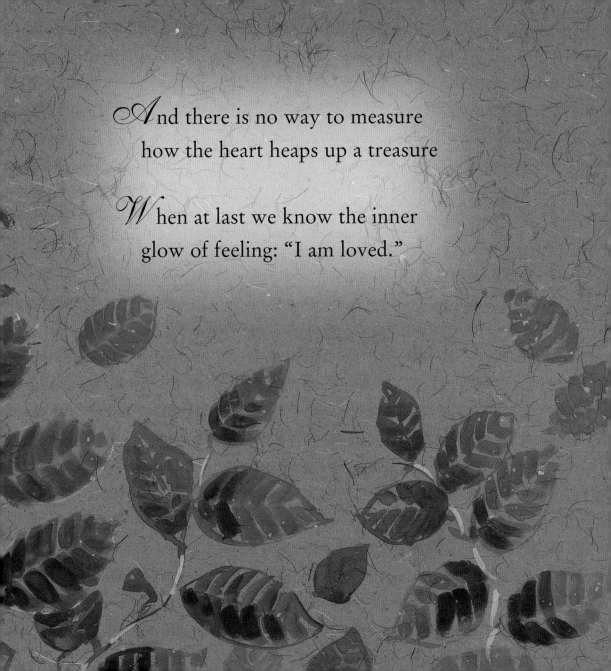

And there is no way to measure
how the heart heaps up a treasure

When at last we know the inner
glow of feeling: "I am loved."

In the glory of a garden
is the tender kiss of spring

And we share a ray of sunshine
with each blossom that we bring

And far more than fragrant flowers,
the gift of self empowers

The heart opens like a rose,
when it knows: "I am loved."

As we're playing with a puppy
or we stroke a kitten's fur

We are welcomed home with
wagging tail or deep, contented purr

When our older pets need kindness,
each devoted look reminds us

Of a wisdom beyond words,
the feeling: "I am loved."

Both the winner of the trophy and the loser in the race

Look beyond the cheering crowds for a special, caring face

I AM® LOVED

And the one who can't fit in,
different feelings different skin

Finds the heart begins to heal
when we feel: "I am loved."

We may talk in different tongues,
we may dress in different clothes

But a smile speaks a language
that everybody knows

And no matter where you roam,
you will find your way back home

To the warm and waiting arms
that make you feel: "I am loved."

*A*nd sometimes all that it takes
is just one courageous deed

*O*r a single act of kindness,
plant a forest with a seed

You can raise hope from the ground, you can turn a life around

You can feel now and forever: "I am loved."